S0-BOB-374

Pocahontas

Adapted for young readers from a Amerindian story

illustrated by Van Gool

© Creation, script and illustrations: A.M. Lefèvre, M. Loiseaux, M. Nathan-Deiller, A. Van Gool
Text adapted for young readers by Duncan Crosbie
First published and produced by **Creations for Children International**, Belgium. www.c4ci.com
This edition published by BPI, India Pvt Ltd
16, Ansari Road, Darya Ganj, New Delhi - 110 002
Tel.: +91-11-2328 4898 • 2327 6118 • Fax: +91-11-2327 1653
Email: bpipl@bpiindia.com • bpiindia@airtelbroadband.in
All rights reserved
Printed in China

Part 1

A new settlement

CHAPTER 1

The coming of the English

One fine spring morning, three English ships sailed into Chesapeake Bay and dropped anchor. After a while, they lowered rowing boats full of soldiers and came ashore. 'Search the surrounding areas,' their captain ordered. 'If there is no sign of danger, the settlers can go ashore.' Hidden in the undergrowth, the native Indians watched. Seeing the men approaching, they drew their bows and arrows and began to shoot. The soldiers replied with rifle fire.

Terrified by these unknown weapons, the Indians fled without looking back. The soldiers explored the land by the sea and the forest behind it without seeing anyone else. They returned to the ships and told the families of settlers that it was safe to go ashore, although they warned them to look out for the Indians, who might come back at any moment. In fact, the Indian warriors had gone straight back

to their village to give their news to Pohatan, the powerful chief of the five Indian tribes, 'They have magic sticks that spit fire and kill from afar,' one of them said. Pohatan was wise and crafty, and he saw at once how valuable it would be to have such weapons. He decided to show a friendly face to the newcomers, hoping that he could get some of these rifles from them before they went home. At his side was his favourite daughter, Pocahontas, who was very interested in the settlers and asked endless questions about them. Within a few weeks the settlers had finished building their fort. Pohatan sent messengers to tell them he would leave them in peace. But each tribe had different customs: some traded with the settlers, exchanging corn and meat for necklaces and beads. Others, despite

Pohatan's promise, attacked them whenever they left the fort. It began to look as if the settlers intended to stay. Pohatan was disappointed. He wanted their powerful weapons, but he also feared that they intended to seize more of his lands. As soon as the settlers tried to cultivate the soil and grow plants, the Indians started to drive them away, and the food began to ran out. Captain Newport and a few other men set off by boat to seek food supplies and help.

CHAPTER 2

The search for food

Captain Newport did not come back. The settlers' food was now reduced to almost nothing. A former officer called John Smith decided to lead a small band inland to search for food: 'We are bound to catch some animals in the forest,' he said. 'Then we will pack the meat in salt so that it lasts. That way we will have enough for the winter.' It was difficult to find enough volunteers, because some were put off by the hostility of the Indians.

But at last the settlers were ready to set out. They pushed their way through the forest, guided by two Indians from a friendly tribe. The heat was stifling, and the English suffered badly in their heavy armour. After many hours they reached the banks of a river. Exhausted by the heat, the men stopped for a while to refresh themselves. They completely forgot to mount a guard, but threw their weapons down on the bank, and gratefully took off their clothes. At that moment, a band of Indian warriors took them by surprise. They had followed the settlers all the way, simply waiting for the right moment to attack. The half-dressed Englishmen had no time to grab and load their rifles. In any case, without their armour they were defenceless against the Indian arrows. The result was a merciless slaughter.

The two Indian guides were also killed. But before he died, one of them cried: 'Leave Captain Smith alive – he is their chieftain!' John Smith was the only one to survive, because the leader of the attackers, Pohatan's brother, dared not kill the chief of the white men. And so John Smith became the first Englishman to set eyes on the village of Werowocomoco, where Pohatan and his large family lived.

When they got back to the village, the prisoner was taken before Pohatan, surrounded by his warriors. Pocahontas was the only woman there. Pohotan asked John Smith if the settlers intended to stay for long. He replied that he felt sure they would leave soon, but Pohatan did not believe him. 'You are going to die, stranger,' he declared. 'Then the other settlers will understand they are not welcome here!'

John Smith was tied to a wooden plank in the middle of the ceremonial tent. Looking at him with hatred, warriors armed with frightening clubs surrounded him. John Smith remained unmoved, showing no fear. Pohatan gave orders for the sentence of death to be carried out. But to everyone's amazement, Pocahontas threw herself across the prisoner to shield him: 'Father,' she cried, 'spare this brave warrior's life!'

Pohatan immediately called back his men and released John Smith. Then he said: 'My daughter Pocahontas believes that you should live, because she can see you are a brave man. According to our customs, you are now free. But you may not leave Werowocomoco.' John bowed to Pocahontas, saying: 'Princess, I owe my life to you, and I will for ever be grateful.'

CHAPTER 3

Learning to love

John Smith lived for a long time in the Indian village. He was free to go where he liked within it, but it was clear there was no intention of releasing him. He often went to the fields with Pocahontas and, because he was interested in other peoples, he learned the customs of the Indians and even a few words of their language. In return, he taught Pocahontas English. Both of them enjoyed each other's company, and soon they were never seen apart.

At last the day came when Pohatan gave John Smith his freedom. 'Now that you understand our customs, I feel sure you will persuade your friends to respect them,' he told him. John replied at once: 'Certainly I will do that, but my words will carry more weight if I can also give them proof of your generosity. Give me food that I can take to the starving settlers.' Pohatan was amazed by the boldness of his prisoner. He thought for a moment and then said: 'White man, I respect your courage, and for that reason you may return with the supplies of food that you and your friends need.' And so John Smith went back to the fort accompanied by Pocahontas and the warriors carrying corn, vegetables and many kinds of meat. The settlers thought John had been killed. They gave him and the young princess a joyful welcome.

Pocahontas stayed in the fort for a while, and then returned home.

A few weeks later, their food supplies were again nearly finished. Suddenly, the sentries shouted a warning that a large group of Indians was approaching. Frightened of an attack, the families took refuge in their houses whilst the soldiers took up position on the walls.

'We shall fight to the death,' they all cried. John Smith was one of those near the front, encouraging the others. But suddenly he was able to call out: 'You can lay down your rifles. These people are our friends!' It was none other than Pohatan and his daughter at the head of a ceremonial column. John Smith put on his best clothes and went forward to meet the Indians of Werowocomoco.

After making a speech of welcome, he invited the chief and his followers to enter the fort. To their delight, the English saw that the warriors were carrying baskets full of every kind of food. Each of the five tribes had provided something to the piles of food heaped before the settlers. There was even seed that they could plant for new crops. Pohatan accepted their thanks graciously.

Indeed, Pohatan had the appearance and bearing of a king, and everyone looked at him with admiration. 'I have come to offer you peace,' he said. 'These presents are the proof of it. But I also wish to be given something in exchange.' John Smith asked him what it was he would like. 'I wish to have weapons that spit fire, like yours,' came the answer. The settlers looked at each other in consternation.

'If we give him what he wants,' they said to each other, 'he'll kill us all!' They all looked towards John Smith. He made a sign to calm them down: 'I have an idea that might make Pohatan abandon his demand,' he said. 'Trust me!' The settlers put him in charge of the talks with the great chieftain. Pohatan happily accepted gifts of jewellery for his family, but it was the rifles he really wanted.

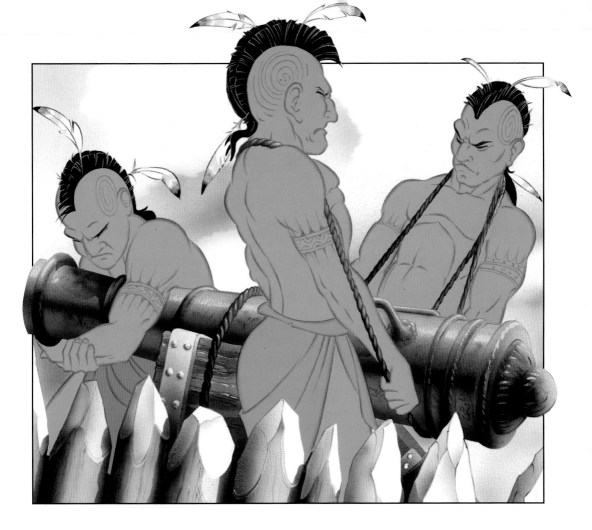

'Alas, I cannot give you the rifles,' John Smith said, looking very sad, 'because they are the only weapons we have to hunt with!' Pohatan then pointed at the cannons standing nearby: 'I want those,' he said. John pretended to look anxious. 'Oh, well. You've won,' he said. 'Your men can take away whatever they can lift.' Pohatan was delighted. But when the warriors tried to lift the heavy cannon, they could not get them off the ground.

John Smith's trick had worked. He said in a serious voice that lighter cannons were being sent from England, and that he would be very pleased to give some to the great chief. Pohatan, who was completely taken in, agreed and returned to Werowocomoco.

Part 2
War and peace

CHAPTER 3

Peace must be saved!

The place that the settlers had built soon became a small town. They called it Jamestown. Pocahontas came often, bringing food and gifts. She was a faithful messenger for her father, and every time she asked for the cannons to be sent to him. John Smith always managed to find an excuse, but by now he had become very fond of this pretty Indian who taught him her language. After a while he began to write a book about Indian life, and even prepared a dictionary of the pohatan language.

In order to feed themselves, the settlers cleared the land surrounding Jamestown, and used the logs to build more houses. They planted the seed given them by Pohatan and looked after their fields. It often happened that Indians attacked them, so the men took their rifles everywhere to protect their new fields. In the eyes of the settlers, their fields had been made in land that nobody owned. But they were really on land that belonged to the five tribes, and Pohatan was upset at the way the English settlement was growing. The settlers no longer spoke of leaving as they had when they first arrived, and the promised cannons did not arrive. The chief called a Great Council, but took care to keep Pocahontas away because he knew of her affection for John Smith. 'My friends,' he said to the other chieftains, 'we cannot allow these strangers to steal our lands!'

Everyone agreed with him, and they decided to attack Jamestown at dawn two days later. Pocahontas suspected some dreadful plot was being hatched. She pretended to go to her tent, but then slipped out to listen and realised what was being planned. 'Our friendship with the strangers will be over, and I will never see John again,' she thought with alarm.

She knew she must do something to stop the two peoples fighting each other, but how could a battle be avoided? There was only one answer: she must warn John Smith. The young girl slipped out of the village, avoiding the sentries, and disappeared into the trees. All night long she ran through the forest by the light of the moon, and reached Jamestown as the sun was rising. The English guards recognised her and let her pass.

Pocahontas found John and told him everything she had overheard. 'Promise not to attack my family,' she begged him. 'I am doing this for peace between us, not to betray them. John swore to Pocahontas that he would tell nobody what she had said, and that no blood would be spilled. Pocahontas returned quickly to her village, where no-one had noticed her absence. She felt sure her clever friend would find an answer to the problem.

John Smith thought hard about it, looking for a way to avoid a battle. He decided to go for a walk in the woods to help him think, and it was there he saw his chance. Two settlers were fishing in the river, and three Indians were getting ready to attack them. John recognised one of them. It was Pohatan's brother. He slid quietly up behind him and pressed his dagger in his back.

'Warriors,' he called to the other two Indians, 'throw down your arms at once, or your leader will die!' John Smith led his three prisoners to Werowocomoco and went to the chief. 'See,' he said, 'your men were about to kill some settlers but I stopped them, and I spared the life of your brother. We have kept our promise to live in peace, but are you going to keep your promise?'

Pohatan was clever enough to see that John Smith had learned about the plans of the five tribes. If he suspected Pocahontas, he said nothing. Pohatan decided to call off the attack. As Indian custom demanded, he and Smith smoked the pipe of peace together, and John returned to Jamestown feeling very relieved. But he knew he had made a terrible enemy of Pohatan's brother, who had been humiliated by being taken prisoner.

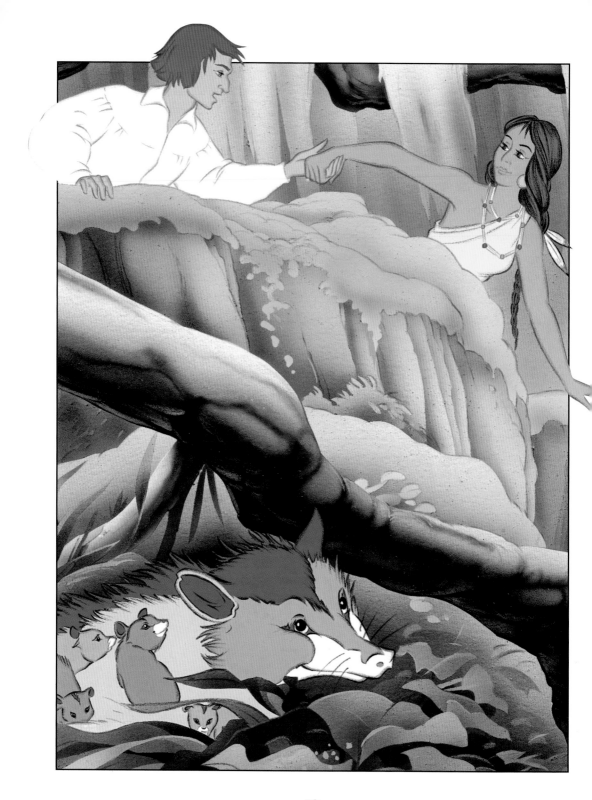

CHAPTER 5

A very sad war

Pocahontas continued to visit Jamestown to see John Smith, of whom she became fonder with every day that passed. Her father allowed these visits, because he still hoped to get weapons. The young woman taught her friend to love the wildlife and the magnificent countryside in this wild part of America. On his side, John told her all about London, the king, and the kind of life the English led. She dreamed of seeing this far-off island with its strange customs, so very different from her own.

Unlike the other settlers, John wanted to stay in America. He loved being with Pocahontas, and enjoyed his important place in the life of Jamestown. The settlers regarded him as their leader because, although he had no official title, only he could speak the language of the Indians and hold discussions with them. But one day a ship arrived carrying new settlers under the command of Captain Argall.

He had orders to prepare for the arrival of a new governor, Lord de la Warr. John saw at once that his importance would soon be over. With great sorrow, he decided to leave Jamestown in order to trade with the Indians. 'Let us go and talk to my brother,' Pocahontas suggested. 'I'm sure he will give you some land. John began a new life, travelling regularly between his new lands and Jamestown.

Pocahontas was now old enough to be married. She went to her father and asked him: 'If John Smith asked me to be his wife, would you accept him?' Pohatan liked John, but not so much that he wanted to give his daughter to him. But he thought about the weapons he still hoped to get and gave a careful reply: 'My child, it is something I must think over. I had wanted to marry you to an Indian of our own tribe, but I could yet change my mind.'

Pocahontas remained in the village while her father decided on her future. A few days later, John Smith went out hunting with some of the other settlers. When they came to a clearing, they felt they were being watched. But before they had time to load their rifles, arrows began raining down on them. It was Pohatan's brother, determined to revenge himself, who led the attack. There was a terrible fight.

John Smith was badly wounded in the chest and collapsed unconscious. The wounded men were carried back to Jamestown. It was now that the boat carrying Lord de la Warr arrived, bringing many new settlers with it. Their orders were to enlarge the town, to develop farms and to control the Indians. Before he was wounded, John Smith had said many times, loud and clear, that the new governor would be unable to talk to the Indians as he could. Lord de la Warr had heard of this challenge to his authority and was very displeased. So when he saw that John was badly wounded, he knew this was a chance to get rid of him.

Pretending he wanted to help him recover his health, he sent him back to England by the same boat that had brought him out. Then he ordered the settlers to tell the Indians that Smith was dead.

CHAPTER 6

An Indian lady

The dreadful news soon reached Pohatan's village. The warriors returning from Jamestown came to warn their chief. 'John Smith is dead,' they said. 'An arrow killed him. The white men put his body on their big boat and took it back to his own country.' Pocahantas was overcome by grief. Her father tried in vain to comfort her, even though he was secretly relieved that John was no longer there. The young woman went to her tent and stayed there for many long days, eating nothing and speaking to nobody.

When she eventually emerged she was pale and thin, but she had recovered her spirits. Like the daughter of a noble chieftain, she accepted what fate had in store for her. To Pohatan she said: 'Father, now that John Smith is dead, I will no longer visit the settlers at Jamestown. You can marry me to whoever you want.' And so she left Werowocomoco in a magnificent procession to join

her future husband, Kakoum of the Patawomeke ribe. With John Smith gone, and Pocahontas no onger in the region, relations between the Indians nd the English became bad. Lord de la Warr had o regard for the Indians and sent a message to ohatan ordering him to hand over to the settlers ll the land they needed. Pohatan was furious. These strangers treat us with contempt and steal ur lands. Let us drive them out once and for all!'

Never a day passed without the English burning down an Indian village, or the Indians attacking the settlers in their fields. Whispers of this cruel war sometimes reached Pocahontas in the far-off place where she now lived. Every evening as the sun went down she sat on a rock looking out over the sea from where her lost love had come, for she had never stopped thinking of him.

Several times, the settlers sent messengers to Pocahontas, saying: 'Princess, you alone can persuade the great chieftain, Pohatan, to stop this fighting.' But always she replied: 'I do not wish to be mixed up in it. My father knows what he is doing.' One day, however, things changed. Kokoum, her husband, died suddenly and she decided to return home to Werowocomoco.

Soon after her return, she became friendly with a settler called John Rolfe. And a few weeks later she married him, with Pohatan's blessing! Their marriage was followed by several years of peace between the settlers and the Indians. Pocahontas had never forgotten all the things John Smith told her about far-away England. 'I want to go there,' she told her husband, 'and see the King.'

And so she and her husband boarded ship for the long journey across the ocean. When she arrived, London seemed even larger and more marvellous than in her dreams. After all, she had seen nothing more than Jamestown. The English treated her as an honoured representative of her people. Poca- ontas was the first Indian to be presented at the urt. Just as she had always hoped, she was able to speak to the King, and he promised to defend the rights of her people. But her greatest joy of all was to discover that the love of her youth, Captain John Smith, was alive and well!